NOT MADE

POETIC MEDITATIONS ON
TIME, SPACE, & OTHER MATTERS

Madeleine (Yeh Jin) Moon-Chun

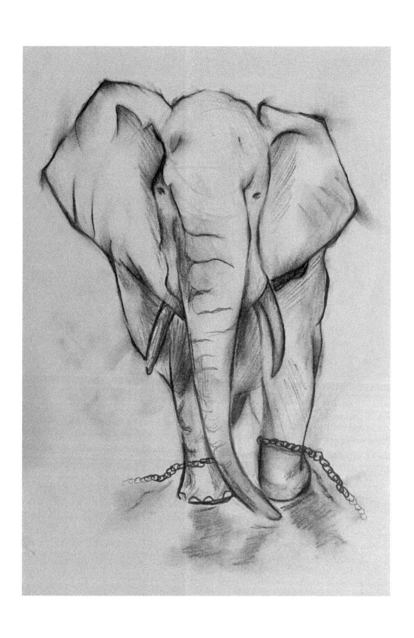

Drawing for Phillip Salzinger's short-term birding class

barred wings

broad wings

Adult

yellow-orange bill

yellow bill

yellow feet

juvenile

NOT MADE OF LINES

POETIC MEDITATIONS ON TIME, SPACE, & OTHER MATTERS

Madeleine (Yeh Jin) Moon-Chun

NOT MADE OF LINES

POETIC MEDITATIONS
ON TIME, SPACE, & OTHER MATTERS

Madeleine (Yeh Jin) Moon-Chun

Eastwind Books | Berkeley | 2024

Published by Eastwind Books of Berkeley
2022 University Avenue, Box 46
Berkeley, CA 94704
www.AsiaBookCenter.com

All text, art and photography by Madeleine Moon-Chun

ISBN: 9781961562073

DEDICATION

To

Tom Painting

Birder, Educator, Poet

EPIGRAPH

Science and art are both concerned

with the continual reorganization

of our conceptual space,

of what we call meaning

—Carlo Rovelli

TABLE OF CONTENTS

About the Author

Madeleine (Yeh-Jin) Moon-Chun is a tenth grader at The Paideia School in Atlanta, GA. In her free time, she likes to read, bike, run, and drink taro bubble tea.

Illustrator & Photographer: Madeleine Moon-Chun

Acknowledgements

I turned twelve years old in an apocalypse. Only, instead of zombies or a stock market crash threatening the foundation of our society, this fear was created amongst ourselves. We feared strangers, neighbors, friends in our concerns about catching the virus. Yes, I think it is safe to say that birding (as well as drawing and writing poetry) kept me sane during the COVID–19 pandemic. The evolutionary history of birds became part of my own story. They were my three ghosts: past, present, and future. When I was little, I had books up to my ears about dinosaurs, elephants, and other aspects of the natural world—whether extinct, endangered, or abundant. At two years old, I knew the difference between the Brontosaurus and Brachiosaurus, and I went to the Atlanta Zoo or the Georgia Aquarium several times a week. When the pandemic hit with aggression, I felt the need to observe the natural world in a—well—natural setting. Fast forward to my current adolescence, and my growing knowledge of birds has fostered a sense of amazement with the human species. Considering all the horrible things humans have done to each other, I am in awe of the good people left. Birds are not so different from us, and the natural world often is reflected in human society, as Shakespeare has explored in several of his plays, such as *Macbeth*. The way we are immensely territorial, attacking constructions greater than ourselves, rivals that of the Northern Mockingbird or Barred Owl in breeding season.

Additionally, with climate change and our ever-growing human population, birds are one of the only creatures left that can be seen in almost every setting. Since we have done some irreversible damage to the environment, I consider birding a hobby, but also a tool to heal the world. We, as humans that caused the extinction of numerous species, need to be aware of the birds in order to prevent this world from falling apart any further.

Ultimately, through poetry and other forms of creative and critical writing, I have been exploring the importance of birds, nature, and community.

Thank you to the many teachers I've had at The Paideia School who have helped me see the wonders that writing brings: Neda, Isabelle, Kristen, Becca, April, and David. The butterfly drawings were done in Aklima Ali's biology class. The Macbeth drawing was done for an assignment in Tally Johnson's English class. The owl drawings were done in Philip Salzinger's short-term high school class.

To Faven and Cassie: Blue Rider club meetings made me look forward to every other Thursday lunch in ninth grade.

Also, I want to acknowledge the Georgia Ornithological Society. They are doing incredible work in promoting the importance of bird survival and the conservation of their habitats. They provide scholarships for students to attend birding camps, including in Maine and Colorado. I was fortunate enough to attend Camp Colorado on a scholarship, where I met some of the most extraordinary birding instructors and campers alike, and I can say that the experience truly changed the way I observe both the natural and human worlds. All author royalties of this book will be donated to the Georgia Ornithological Society for the wonderful efforts they put into helping preserve and spread the beauty of the natural world.

I want to thank Jennie Duberstein, JB Brumfield, Jake Mohlmann, Sebastian Moreno, and Patrick Maurice at Camp Colorado for being such kind and knowledgeable birding mentors. Some of the poetry/prose in this book was inspired by my time at camp.

Thank you to Benjamin, my favorite (and only) baby brother, who makes me laugh to no end and lets me read his short stories. Forever thanks to Hellena Moon and Elbert Chun for being the most supportive and loving parents, walking with me on the continuous journey that is writing/ life. I want to thank my mom for her copy editing and editorial support.

I am so grateful to Tom Painting—to whom this book is dedicated. He was my wonderful seventh/eighth grade teacher and my mentor for both birding and poetry. You kept your homebase door open before school hours and whenever. You continued to help me be a better writer even after I left Junior High.

Thank you, Tom.

Reprints

"Ephemeral Beauty" was first published in the 2022 Regional Scholastic Writing Award magazine (Gold Key award). I want to thank the Alliance for Young Artists and Writers for their generosity in allowing its republication here.

"Time Flies on Feathered Wings" was first published for the Georgia Ornithological Society's Newsletter, *GOShawk*. September 2023, vol. 50, No. 3, p. 6. An abbreviated version appears here.

A few of the haiku are revisions of previously published haiku in Hellena Moon & Emmanuel Lartey's co-edited anthology, *Postcolonial Practices of Care: A Project of Togetherness during COVID-19 & Racial Violence*. Pickwick Publications: Eugene, OR 2022.

"The Runner" was first published in the 2022 Regional Scholastic Writing Award magazine (honorable mention). I want to thank the Alliance for Young Artists and Writers for their generosity in allowing its republication here.

Many of the poems here have been submitted to the 2024 Scholastic Writing Awards. As this book was going to print, I was notified about the following poems winning awards in the Regional Scholastic Writing Award (Atlanta, GA):

1. Gold Key: "Flower Girl"
2. Gold Key: "prayer to the nightingirl"
3. Gold Key: "Sea Star"
4. Gold Key: "the butterfly jar"
5. Silver Key: "atom"
6. Silver Key: "Not Made of Lines"
7. Silver Key: "the animal"
8. Honorable Mention: "the memory of water"
9. Honorable Mention: "Women's Night"

Introduction

Matter, energy, space, and time: these concepts are all forms of one thing. Energy is expressed in our emotions. Our emotions are possible through our energy and our matter and how we take up space. This collection of poetry, prose, haiku, and art are manifestations of my very humble understanding of quantum physics that exist on every level of our world and beyond.

It is difficult to parse out the components of the universe, but I do for organizational purposes. But you, the reader, will see how entangled the components are. Additionally, my prose, poetry, and art demonstrate the importance of how the humanities and science are enmeshed.

Technology continuously improves our lives, and it has become the driving force in our society. With new scientific discoveries and medical advances, more people are focusing on science—and the humanities are becoming less popular in education. I am someone who enjoys and sees the value in "both" fields because, despite how different they appear, both are forms of self-exploration. Ultimately, science aims to uncover everything inside of humans—past, present, and future—to understand the world in which we live. Without the humanities and the cultivation of empathy to drive our ever-expanding scientific knowledge, we would suffer as a species. Similarly, I write poetry with strong themes tied to my understanding of scientific theories and mathematics. Science is not better than the other (humanities); rather, they are better when integrated.

Is science still science without humans? Science was created to satisfy the curiosity of our own human desire, but now as technology has advanced, artificial intelligence is performing many of the tasks we used to do. Where there was room for error in shaking hands and miscalculations, there is now comfort in being cared for by something far less likely to make a mistake. Deep compassion is part of our mortality that robots cannot recreate, and, as a poet who routinely explores the importance of ethics and empathy in science, I hope to further convince you (the reader) how science is a deeply human practice.

PART ONE
TIME

last goodbyes
my white rose disappears
with the dirt

Not Made of Lines

They tell stories
of children growing up
to be princesses or noble knights
in a lifelong search
for enlightenment
and a "Happily Ever After."
They tell stories of aging witches
who are scorned and fated
to an eternal loop of failure,
because a circle
is the most complicated shape.

As a child, I only knew lines.
During batting practice, my softball coach told me
not to drop my hands
because the shortest distance from point A
to point B
is a straight line.

I urge myself to draw in pen sometimes
so I won't obsess over every imperfect line
and have the luxury
to start again.

But we are not made
of straight lines.
Our pupils are round

no beginning or end
to tell a stranger
the extent of our knowledge.
But, centuries ago, revered mathematicians
discovered the word
"pi."
An irrational number
that goes on forever
and ever,
leaps and bounds beyond the lengths
of our subjective wisdom
and mundane comprehension.
The circles that make us up
have an area
of πr^2
With just a middle
to tell us who we are now.

When I was ten years old, I visited my 할아버지,[1]
my grandfather, in Korea.
He was weak,
pale,
and scarred
like the flimsy table next to his wheelchair.
This table held a small round cake wrapped in shiny
red paper,
left over from someone else's lunch.
My 할아버지 could not eat, but his wide round eyes con-
veyed a desire

---

1 In English, it is pronounced, "hahl-ah-buh-jee."

I thought belonged only to
children.

Now, years later, my thoughts still circle back
to how much my 할아버지 reminded me
of a baby.
And how we are only born wanting.
But later, some of us learn that there is more to life
than longing—
the feeling in-between.
Others go on, growing a shell that hardens them
to the suffering of others,
where their ears hear nothing but their own cries
of victory.
And that "want"
in their heads turns to an uncontrollable
desire.

This ephemeral strength
and passionate vitality
that comes with youth and even middle age
circles back to who we were
before.
Only, instead of soft skin
developing muscles and brains,
growing teeth,
and supple bones,
time wrinkles our bodies,
and deteriorates our minds,
where our muscles are atrophied
from lack of use.

Pain assails
our arthritic joints, while we lay in railed beds.

Why must old age be scorned
while youth is cherished and revered?
Why must the elderly be met with disdain
and correlated with taking what shouldn't be theirs?
Because stories are told about the old "evil" witch
who is blind to everything
but what she wants—youth.
To look in the mirror
and see wrinkles around your previously
brilliant eyes and unblemished lips,
to hear muffled nonsense or silence instead of
clear song.

Yet when one sense is weakened,
others are strengthened.
Because if you look deep down in both eyes,
you will only see the same person.
Arched lines make circles
a space for enlightenment
from the loop we are stuck in.
Like caged hamsters endlessly running,
while outside time seems to…
hold its breath.

String Art

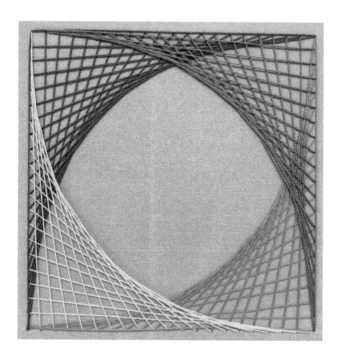

the memory of water

i step to the edge of the water
and remember what it felt like
to sink below this life.

                              yes—we die every day.
i say *breathe*, and really i mean:
remember that blood only slows down enough
to reassure the survivor's reflex in this body,

if only it were that easy.

i watch the birds in the sky above me
and breathe out wishes that break with childhood, fear not;
become sad for what they must know.

but is knowledge in a broken body
something to celebrate or mourn?

i wonder whether suffering   is instinct   or desire

when instinct—
tell me why preservation has become so selfless,
why we watch others die,
                  instead of ourselves.

when desire—
        ask me if pain has a sound other than *silenced*. yes,
    my breath comes in bubbles towards the surface

like rain reversed,

        rising as smoke does,

and like smoke,

        hurts too much to remember.
remember… that innocence is nothing
without memory.

Women's Night

Tonight is our night, June twenty-fourth.
Women's night.
My mother drives us down the winding path
towards the home of our
matriarch.
The road is empty—
trees on one side, a small pasture on the other.
Two horses watch the cars fly by
from the grassy side of the road.
Are they siblings?
A mother and her daughter?
Though in the barn most weekends,
today they walk the length of the uneven fence
that is just high enough
to keep them in.
It is old wire with a coat of rust not quite thick enough
to hide the scars it bears.
Time to take it down,
time for change,
but it seems as though we like to keep
what remains the "foundation"
of this farm.
Three generations of women sit at the table.

My mother—
a daughter for those few precious moments—
brings fish to the table.
It is unusually large,
and we rip away its bones
like branches from trees we don't hesitate to uproot
to get the soft fish underneath.
This was once a female flounder.
We see the pale masses in its underbelly,
all the eggs that never left.
We eat them anyway,
for they were not yet fish.

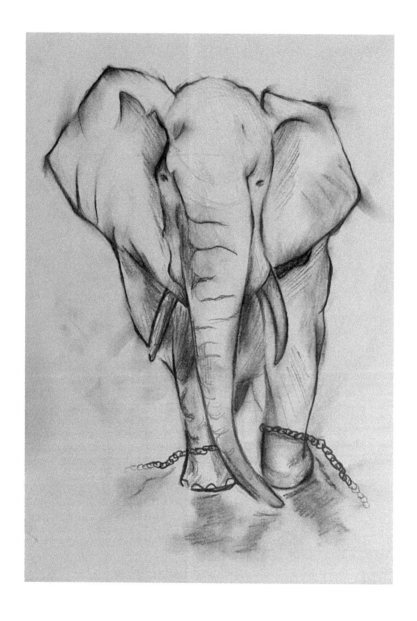

Ephemeral Beauty[2]

in the mountains up north
fall glows golden
then orange
like drops of fire

salmon migrate
from rivers to the sea
their flanks red—
like the color of blood
brushed with silver

winter, too, harbors many wonders
rivers swell with blocks of ice
and tree branches bend
with the weight of snow

then spring comes
on the warming wind
that carries far with cries
of courting creatures

slate-gray streams froth
with the intake
of melting snow
ice sculptures remain

---

2   This poem was written in Tom Painting's 8th grade class. It won the
Gold Key award in the Scholastic Writing Award, 2022.

as thin and clear
as a looking glass

by summer
the mountains reach their prime
brooks bubble over
as if to call forth attention to themselves

the foothills
dotted with small purple flowers
hang on delicate stems
like teacups

Time Flies on Feathered Wings[3]

Raucous calls of Black-billed Magpies pierce through our white rental car, bringing me out of a combination of entranced reverie, nerves, and excitement. Here at the YMCA of the Rockies, snow-threaded mountains undulate the continuous blue sky in the distance. We are a mile closer to the sun than back home. After saying goodbye to my family, one of the instructors walks me and another young birder towards where we will be staying, Twin Sisters. The quarter mile walk takes us ten minutes, stopping to observe the abundant Common Ground Squirrels, Broad-tailed Hummingbirds, and Black-billed Magpies. The magpies, especially, catch my eye—their glossy, blue-black bodies, white flanks, and long, iridescent wings and tail catch the Saturday afternoon sun as they hop gracefully and unafraid along the path in front of us. With two lifers in the span of ten minutes, I can tell this will be a good week.

Introductions come after we transport food and luggage to the meeting room in the basement of Twin Sisters. At dinner, we bring trays and sit at picnic tables outside with Broad-tailed Hummingbirds, House Sparrows, Mountain Bluebirds, White-crowned Sparrows, American Crows, and,

---

3 This is a revised version of what I wrote for the Georgia Ornithological Society's Newsletter, *GOShawk*. September 2023, vol. 50, No. 3, p. 6.

yes, more Black-billed Magpies, to name a few. Orientation back in the fireside meeting room is kept brief as possible to ensure we have enough time to sleep before our busy day tomorrow.

With our eyes behind binoculars, we miss the days flying by on swift, sure wings. So before I know it, Wednesday comes. Our so-called "Big Day" is the longest—and my favorite—day. My roommates and I set our alarms for 4:15 A.M. and are in the white vans by 4:45. We stop on a gravel road in Weld, Colorado, for Baird's Sandpipers, Horned Larks, Lark Sparrows, Lark Buntings, Blue-Winged Teals, and the ever-so-elusive Sora. In Briggsdale, we are met with Mountain Plovers, Loggerhead Shrikes, Western Meadowlarks, and many Horned Larks. We spend the majority of our day driving in the seemingly endless grassland of the Pawnee, fulfilling one camper's birthday wish to see a Burrowing Owl.

Through meeting my wonderful fellow campers, they show me how much we may see but still miss until we really try and look. Here at Camp Colorado, I find that time is a rare and secretive bird. It passes us by, quietly, in tall grass or shadow right under our noses, and by the time we see it, precious flight feathers have already taken it high above our heads.

Black-billed Magpie near picnic tables at our last breakfast (Camp Colorado)

Western Kingbird at the Rabbit Mountain parking lot on a Sunday (Camp Colorado)

American Goldfinch

PART TWO
MATTER

home from the hospital[4]
the new father
plants a birch tree

---

4   This haiku was previously published in Moon & Lartey, *Postcolonial Practices of Care*, 143.

the butterfly jar

before i knew that veins
were more violent than rivers, i taught my hands
to sew and break string, not to bind
but to free, made a rope to keep us away from the sun,
thought to heal the hurt, the lonely, alone,
tame the river of blood
and wash the scars

before i learned i could not
even help the torn butterfly, my fingerprints cut
its gossamer wings like a thousand paper cuts.
the bloodless whispered that small pain
would never be more than a passing joke.

before i knew that lost language could be a martyr,
i learned knowledge isn't always power,
it's isolation. i wonder if being happy
is rationally dependent
on how well we know sadness, how well we know
the period between when darkness refuses
to offer us respite
and when the sun flees our dirty fingertips.

I'd like to think that anyone who's held a butterfly
knows what the darkest hour really means.
because i've watched you ride through the fields,
trampling undiscovered grass under your numb

bicycle tires. all around, butterflies tremble
the darkening blueness, escaping you,
the racing twilight. only a beautiful time
because language
is glamoured pain.

floating in the masses
behind our wake, the insects disturbed
by our careless ways
remind me of the birds
who offered "freedom," uncaged
but always tethered.
happy because twilight is all they know. they can play
to the illusion they are given. because this country
is the land of butterflies,
our scars not yet healed fit so easily
in the mason jar.

we cover the lid
with red cloth and a tight seal. this butterfly is beautiful
like everything without a voice. only beautiful
until contradiction, when pain is the spectacle
on screen. we watch it just because it's on,
because we know nothing
beyond touching brightness, and dusk
is approaching.

and as i watch this butterfly,
i think about how its life
is just a production. beauty is how well you can layer
pretense over pain.

and i think about how you love to love the easiest things.
people who have no choice
but to love you back. and twilight
instead of the darkest hour because complacency
in half-happiness is more
than faith or hope
which sneer away a flaking protection.
and the butterfly with torn wings
because you know it can never fly away. always
a servant to your happiness.

because our bodies
are broken butterflies, moving wings
against the beat of the battered skin
'til day reaps the protection of darkness.
a servant to this happiness till the river runs dry.

because i know
that we were the ones who cut the butterfly.
folded its wings into this watery glass to hide
the brave martyr, drown desire. because i know
that knowing leaves behind
the deepest impression we hold,
that it bleeds the longest
because it is the part of our body
the heart is most reluctant to give away.

When the butterfly emerges from chrysalis, her wings are crumpl' and wet. She must wait for a hours, clinging to the rem of her chrysalis, for her to harden enough for flight. She pumps flu from the abdomen to flow through wings to expand

rfly's final her only food lectar. Being a neration Monarch ly only live for a few weeks. In this time, she, too, y hundreds of eggs in the shade the undersides of milkweed leaves.

Drawings for a biology project: Aklima Ali's class

The female Monarch butterfly

the animal

i turn on the faucet in the downstairs bathroom
to the hottest it can go. i think all bathrooms are shrines
and altars,
temples for preservation of change. i watch the steam rise
as the water warms, and i can only imagine a waterfall. how
it's so beautiful, but only
for the moment before you fall. how temporary
that it seems there should be more to water than falling. all
i can touch
is the aftermath of the storm, caress the animal after it has
fallen, as if the action
shadows the outcome. all i can feel is what water is like
after the fire. this sanctity is nothing if not brokenness
disguised as savior. i run my hands under the scald-
ing water.
my fingertips turn red. in biology, we learned that the
human body
has trillions of cells. i know that blood is over ninety per-
cent water.
we are more grounded than we like to believe. and our
hearts carry this trauma
to all of our organs and expect a reprieve, and i've touched
the backbone
of the monster far too many times to accept that the unfor-
givable in us
is a result of tainted water. i look in the mirror, at this
skin—this buffer

which is only successful in shaping the animal. my
hands are hot
under the water, the only moments of warmth they receive
besides those in sleep,
in ignorance, because my body is a broken security gate;
it refuses to help the skin it knows is helpless.
the droplets spin toward the drain
with a migratory desperation and my hands grab at
the water
as if to protect the animal who knows it is destined to fall.
people ask me why i don't usually share my poetry.
it is the reason i do not let you examine my hands
and why i do not hug very well. by touching this skin,
you are opening the door to the closet
or lifting the blankets to see under the bed because i can
only guarantee
the monster. metaphor.
but i will reach out with these hands, caress the animal
before it falls.
in my favorite memory, i am small, hands scarless
and whole
and i watch my grandmother stand at her bathroom sink.
she coats her face religiously
with lotions and creams to make herself appear ageless.
wipes her hands to erase the wrinkles,
the memories. as if our real nightmare
were not the supernatural but the mundane.
as if clean hands and smooth skin remove us from
the premise
where the monster roams uncaged. i turn off the faucet

and wonder how many cells i've lost. how i have
never given
or gotten any flowers, even in death. because i, too, wash
this skin
to preserve the altar and become a witch only in the sense
of fearing death.
because i guess that to love something as temporary as skin
is to embrace the animal's memory, even as it flees.

lungs

the little bird flits between the bars of her cage
pink feet somehow grasp twenty-four beams
all at once
and squeeze
they make rattling sounds
that echo against stone walls
like shuddering breaths
an impromptu performance
of sinewy trees crackling and stretching
from the weight in the air
it has many branches that run with sand
the growing mounds pile up beneath her skin
so other birds hold their breath
know to save the sounds
for when doors close at night
then they breathe
to expand the bars
and preach and preen and pluck
and the dunes are quiet once more
despite the keys they drop, their careless beaks
dig deep in the soft shore sand
no one knows about the breaking
and entering
of the mind
i, too,
breathe the only way i know
air passes through jagged lungs

pink feet push against the bars that shrink
while dropping sand echoes behind its muffled skin
i take out the bird and hold her
shivering with my own cold hands
i free her head
and breathe out like i've been taught

atom

if you wear something long enough,
it becomes part of you. if we turn far enough
away from the sun, you can call this
night. dirt and rock, all angles, become
soft when it is shadow that is
for once, the center point,
and not light. if i stare
at your face long enough, i can
make it disappear.
my fingers burn
holding bread straight
from the toaster.
sharp hair brushes my neck,
simultaneously entangling itself
with the clasp of a necklace.
it holds back my neck.
i touch hands with my mother,
feeling how the ridges of our fingerprints
are shaped so similarly
against each other—
you tell me none of this
is real.
you breathe deeply
to fill your lungs
and yet, you say
that the sweat
carving a ticklish path

down my hairline is merely
the wishful thinking
of imaginary senses.
tell me love is no more tangible
than the whispering thoughts
that we are a collection of atoms
floating in the vast cistern of emptiness
invisible to our naked eyes
so longing for touch
and refusing to collide

whole full of holes

i didn't know a river
could be so quiet. i watch the sun,
how its previously believed
omniscient fingertips probe the water,
a futile effort. and yet, we stand
above its deepest parts, ankles wobbling
to steady us in the boat.
we stare down in its depths.
the longer we look, the more
we only see the reflection
showing us—wavering clouds
above our heads;
> distortion of sight is the most disturbing
> loss of the senses.

rippling reflections let us choose,
for once, who we will become.
by which i mean: we are so far
from free.

naturally, i stand staring, hoping
for a clearer glance
that will not come.
praying, maybe, for lightness
if my prayers are just glorified pleas
to watch my own voice
disappear into the void.

promised nothing, but hoping so.
     and i know that hope
     was the only spirit left in pandora's box.
     (they knew what ~~beauty~~ danger was.)

i am drawn back
to the moments spent in my bedroom
when i couldn't sleep. i would turn
on my lamp and look in the mirror
just to check that i was still there.

because even as i pinch my skin, i know
we are only complicated recyclings
of a greater story:
     (matter cannot be created
     or destroyed).

maturation means to stop
praying for the past, grieve someone
whom i have not yet lost
     (i know we mourn the concept
     of our youth—haphazard sketches
     whose pencil marks ~~heal~~ fade
     with time because they were
     never meant to stay.)
it means looking away from the mirrors
and trying to remember it for ourselves,
just once
.

and yet, maturing means that,
too often, we turn to make peace

with our shadows.
by which i mean: we are moving forward
too fast
to even see our skin.

but it is only the rethinking of space
that brings meaning to matter.

around me, i know we are all here
at the water for one reason:
we are terrified of what it means
when even a reflection
can't tell you who you are.
obsession writes off all other cares
as inconsequential.
and yet, consequence is what
gives beauty meaning.
it will have no reason
to stay without a risk.
we can make it last longest
in empty spaces
such as these;
        it can echo,
        as hope does.

we are black holes who give
instead of take; incomprehensible beings
whose matter may
bring meaning to emptiness.

meaning we understand that little

which is whole can be understood.
and emptiness can be loved
if it is given a face.

so we scream, but no one will hear
from behind the wall of water,

so we look in the mirror.
once again, the river—
we toss skipping stones
onto our own faces
and smile.

PART THREE
SPACE

waning moon[5]
on a deserted road
taillights fade into black

---

5 This haiku is a revision of a previously published haiku I wrote. See Moon & Lartey, *Postcolonial Practices of Care,* 27.

Rain

i watch you walk away
in the pouring rain. you hold a red umbrella in your left
hand, as if
it remains the sole connection to your god, lets you know
there's no difference between lifeline or religion. it
is a color
that would be beautiful
if i had someone else's eyes, and i see your white shoes
kick up mud along the path of my flooded garden.
you hated rain and dirty shoes, and the dream-like
part of me
wonders why anyone would induce upon themselves
what they dislike. it reminds me
that passion is just a process of extended separation. i see
your back,
shadowed against the gray sky,
shrink with every added footprint. by the pull in my
chest, i have
no choice but to follow you. my eyes are drawn
towards the red thing you hold in your hand,
and i think that you must carry it because it looks
like blood, maybe reminds you that we are all still alive–
coursing. or maybe you carry it
because beautiful people are too self-deprecating. around
your hunched shoulders,
sacrality weaves its forbidden name
between every tendril of wind. i want to know

everything you've ever kept from me. and so, we come to
the ocean. it is here
that i wonder if loneliness
is to pour too much passion into someone else,
if it is the love i didn't know to give myself
left to in this space, this void, between me and you. it rains
harder now,
pushing pins on my eyelids like sorrow
could reach her hands into my brain. the rain burns my skin
like snow on new blood, and i remember the times
we caught snowflakes on our tongues.
when we thought it was sugar from the sky.
when we thought that words were temporary.
i sprint to catch up with you
and your closed fist
and your red umbrella, but you step into the frothing waves
and throw that hand into the sky. rain falls so fast
it hurts my skin. and as you turn to look at me, with the
same string
on your chest and that strange half-faced smile,
rictus and hovering, your umbrella tearing itself apart
in the wind
reminds me that passion is pain.
reminds me that we were once rain, too.

Flying Home

The pigeons who grew up one summer
outside my grandma's front porch windowsill always knew
how to get back home.
I wonder about the doves who watch us
from the telephone wires, clinging eyes
in the night sky, all fleeting wings and hesitant decisions—
either fleeing or coming back home,
I cannot say. They fly in flocks
because proximity is the only home
they know. I wonder if *home* to everyone
who outgrew acceptance is a story
of falling birds
and flying ones. Some tell me
we all have a spirit animal, that opposites
attract and collide. My spirit is an animal, feathers
whispering
at the nearing ground that *home* is not a place
but a choice, that ambition always aims for the eye of
the storm,
always falling. I travel in a flock
because it is the only home
I know. When I reach the telephone wire,
I balance with grasping feet
too small to carry my weight. Too close to falling,
too close to happiness—wild and untamed and self-serving
as if guided by a broken compass. Forever north,
always leading towards my homeland.

fall

we are rain, like everything else
that can be compared to imperfection.
touch your finger to the puddle
watch yourself peel away in ripples
behind a one-way glass like someone
you used to know. because rain is deceptive,
like destiny.

when the rain falls in sheets
gray clouds grow thicker like cumulus' better cousin
and yet we call this
anger.
praising the sun,
we soak up its warmth on our bare backs
until we resemble that which we hold
sacred.

say it was temporary.
say the burns on your body peeled away to show new skin
and not a cancerous diagnosis.
tell me all this and don't say it was
happiness
that brought you
here.

the first rain looks so heavy it almost reflects,
holds your face in its gaze,

destined to fall.
danger holds no jurisdiction here
empty sidewalks with no trace
of red, and yet you walk your children
back to the house to watch… once
from the inside out.
for "to jump" means having no fear of what happens
when you come back down
and "twirling" means having enough space
to look both ways.

Sea Star

hands find the towel on the beach at low tide
and raise it above the empty being
that is you

it is a silver wing to drum
the stretch of shore into almost-silence, except
pouring wind and the waves, a harmonious breath
inviting us to dance:
what is the sound of two objects never colliding?

like the moon whose careful steps
leave a distorted triangle on the waves
that are gray in the low light,

telling me of the bird somewhere
up in the star explosions
and black holes who reveals distortions of the only
two concepts
we consider to be absolute:
time and space

vengeful flashing wings
stir placid salt
into a torrent almost as constant
as stardeath

and in this brief moment, you are glad

that you are on the sand—
far from water bewitched
by silver talons, hooked beaks,
because the ocean is a fearful place

like how iciness from the stars above us
match the multitudes of the sand, trillions of unmapped
existences,

lived and lost
and transformed,
black holes created and forgotten by your own toes
in the muddied grains far from the sand dunes
where it's safe

and then the darkness is expanding

warmed water pulls in the masses
pushing for more
in the unbalanced and misplaced confidence
that is gravity
the bird's great silver wing is soft on your hot
sand-scratched back
she guides you towards the froth and grime and purity
and you let her

because you're breaking, you're breaking

but in the approaching quietude,
if you turn to face the ocean,
and let the tormented salt

wash over your ears, you can almost miss
the bobbing flashlights
and rogue footfalls
on the stretch of shore behind

PART FOUR
ENERGY

crowded feeder[6]
a blackbird steals
the last seed

6   This haiku is a revision of a previously published haiku I wrote. See
Moon & Lartey, *Postcolonial Practices of Care,* 117.

The Runner[7]

as night came
and ocean waves calmed
the runner appeared
silhouetted against
the rising moon

bare footed and agile
their steady heart pumped
like a ticking clock

they left shallow footprints
in the packed sand
all traces of them gone
with the next wave

they moved with purpose
long hair billowing
behind them
like a proud flag
raised and let fly

out there
between silver, arching sand dunes
and moonlit water
they were alone

7　This poem was written in Tom Painting's 8th grade class. It won honorable mention in the Scholastic Writings Awards, 2022.

they ran for miles
going strong along the shore
until the moon fell and the sun rose

then the universe blurred their
lines and shapes
until runner and earth
became one and the same

bomb

my mother told me that ginkgos
are the oldest species of tree
they have little fan-shaped leaves
that turn milky yellow before they fall
which they would not, gray-brown bark
still twisting in the ash and falling bodies

Deception

A thin sheen of ice
across the broad frozen lake
playful steps pay the price
as the opaque crystal breaks

across the broad frozen lake
the cracks slowly grow
as the opaque crystal breaks
dark water starts to flow

the cracks slowly grow
across the thin sheet of ice
dark water starts to flow
you'd better think twice

A Bag of Traits

dripping in the deepest cave
frozen atop the tallest mountain
moving between thin air
and rich earth.
a thirst quencher
a heart-breaker
a healer…
and a killer.

on the shore of the ocean
at the edge of the world
little birds flock at the water's edge
jumping out of reach every time a wave
comes crawling up the shore.
the foamy bubbles gently nip
at their talons
and erase the footprints they leave behind—
stronger than anything
that ever tried
to beat it.

between icy moonlight and cold earth
runs a river filled with secrets.
rising up only
when the world becomes too dark to notice.

the bubbling of streams

a language
open only to those who aim
to see the glass half full.

the child who sits alone
by the half-frozen lake
already knows more than we will
in a lifetime…
for they understand
what water has to say.
and the child who stands
in the pouring rain
is happier than all those who only want
what they will never have
or lose themselves
in the storm of the process
while trying.

the sand and the sea—
a mother and her child.
what would the ocean be
without the shore
to guide?

feathery snowflakes drift down in flurries
that cover the earth
in a seamless white blanket.
the flakes land on my eyelashes
boots
and bare hands
as i desperately run and try to catch

the pieces of delicate beauty
and perfection we are so quick to
call a storm.

icicles hang from rooftops
suspended in cold, dangerous glory.
mesmerizing
and terrifying
and beautifully dark
despite the brightness
to an unassuming eye.
a moment frozen in time
a memory of how things were
a reminder for how things could have been
a warning to something that still has yet to come.

in a dark cave beneath the surface
blind salamanders can see more
than we.

but the life that pulses
in the depths of their being
refuses to stop
in the damp earth beneath.
a rhythm not seen nor heard...
only felt and remembered
by the hearts of those
who can be satisfied.

dripping in the deepest cave
frozen atop the tallest mountain

moving between thin air
and rich earth.
a thirst quencher
a heart-breaker
a healer...
and a killer.

Flower Girl

this time, water doesn't stop at the skin.
my feet slide on low grass and slippery cliffs. the sky
is a flower, open wounds gaping
and gathering strength. petals reach down,
too shy to touch the ocean
but torment it from a distance
anyway.
proximity is a weapon,
and we have let ourselves
be hurt too many times.
soften your edges,
hide the way this closeness
is an art we were never meant to learn.

this is the hymn that spurred the Wanting.

i know that the ocean
is always disappointed. she tells me
i do not know
what love is. so i watch her
and mold my hand into a bird
the shape desire always makes
in reflection. fingers splayed, ready to catch
the water in droplets that killed so many.
i sacrifice breath.

open my mouth to taste what love must be

and choke on salt.
crystallized loss
oversaturated its great body.
my wrist flicks in anticipation.
i will be the first to know that love
is an elegant torment of desire, know that credence
only ever goes half the distance. dark sky hangs low
across the water. she prepares the stigma
to feel its movement.

i know it was necessity that spurred the Leaving.

clouds part. gulls cry
what must be the highest song
of belief. the sun reaches down
and touches the flower. she falls,
spreads her arms
to feel the fire, for she knows that full pain
is happiness's predecessor.
that no life is worth the tether.

i jump, feel the rocks cut my feet on the Leaving.

fingers splayed, ready to catch the last burning petal
before it becomes another gravestone,
another mark of the elegant torment of desire.

prayer to the nightingirl

the world still turns as it should.
so in the fading light, i see her speak. a borrowed tongue
doing the only job it knows. her words slip past
guarded teeth.
water knitting itself
between each broken syllable.
dark waves push the sand away, deeper
and deeper, until i see the river she points to,
hear the doves mourn nightfall with the wind.
i reach out my hand and calm the animal,
cup my hand against her gray face,
twisting angel hair between shadowed fingers,
sounding like laughter.
i move closer,
touching fear, a soft feathered animal with leaping veins
and open in all the right places.
she lets me
and quells the swelling
twisting mass that is the water,
while redness spreads down by the bank
and slithers away from the waves
with swift fingers that squeeze roping muscle fibers,
erode bone
but quietly
mixing blood in a burning pot under the skin,

and yet
this chaos is lovely
because it is invisible
tearing apart from the inside.
beauty must be the bridge connecting bliss and
consequence.
she steps on it.
her words drip loudly
on the stone,
echoing like the sound emptiness would make,
if only it had a voice.
i know we stand between this burning world and the next,
hopscotch planets and rearrange
constellations, i know
that sometimes we soften
towards the animal we know is helpless
because it gives us relief:
caress the numb faces,
burn the freezing bodies.
perhaps the god made a mistake
giving us flame to hold in our palms
when sympathy always gives way to forest fire
and everything good will leave its burn mark
in the shadow of consequence.
safe from the fire, she reaches the end of the bridge.
i am close enough to feel her breath
to touch fear, that soft feathered animal
veins slowed to exhaustion
opened in all the right places.
she points to the bird

that casts its shadow over her body,
all cheekbones and glittering teeth

Macbeth: Tally Johnson's class assignment

ZOO

all day, we hear the animal pacing.
she traces the length of the glass first
(the one that looks into the leopard's cage
if you position yourself
right. the one that only takes four paces
to cross). what little light/life
in the day
that is left
shows up in her eyes,
reflected.

she watches us
from her side of the glass,
head dipped
and mouth hanging open.
everyone just says she is hungry,
how much she is ready
for a delicious meal prepared
by loving hands.

clamoring kids (whose favorite animal
changes with every exhibit)
smudge up the glass
with fingerprints saturated by cotton candy
remnants, breathing heavily on the glass
and drawing hearts

around kittens or names
with the condensation.

the animal turns
toward the glass, going back
the way she came.
the only way she can.
in a few moments,
the kids will turn toward their parents
with those same sticky fingers
and now-tired eyes
that beg to go home.

she would give anything
to be tired
or go home.
so she doesn't stop pacing, only moving
her eyes to watch the families
walk away
and keep walking.

if you think love is feather-light,
then desire is the heaviest brand of hope
and jealousy the hardest,
full of patched fur and atrophied limbs
worn rock-stiff.

now, you ask
why we are afraid of deep water,
why we love fire
to light up moonless nights.

it is why
we fear the animal with concealed fangs,
those silent paws and sad eyes.
the animal who bites its own tail
and leaves hair chunks in every corner
of the cage.
the one we keep
behind thick glass
and a dried-up moat.

in the wake of stumbling kids
and sweating parents,
your back to the pacing animal,
you reassure yourself.
yes, by morning,
the glass will be clean again.

CODA

Carolina Wren

Barred Owl

Drawing for Phillip Salzinger's short-term birding class

Milton Keynes UK
Ingram Content Group UK Ltd.
UKHW021859310524
443315UK00009B/63

9 781961 562073